READ·WELL®

UNITS 11, 12, 13 STORYBOOK

Mammals

ISBN 13: 978-1-59318-334-9
ISBN 10: 1-59318-334-8
131588

Printed in the United States of America
Published and Distributed by

D1406577

17855 Dallas Parkway, Suite 400 • Dallas, TX 75287 • 800 547-6747
www.voyagersopris.com

UNIT 11 • All About Mammals

Planning Assistance: See Daily Lesson Planning for scheduling the Summary and Extra Practice.

UNIT 12 • Mammal Pets

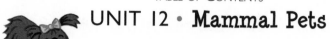

Planning Assistance: See Daily Lesson Planning for scheduling the Summaries and Extra Practice.

UNIT 13 • Mammals in Winter

Where to Live?

Half In and Half Out

Planning Assistance: See Daily Lesson Planning for scheduling the Summary and Extra Practice.

All About Mammals

By Marilyn Sprick and Ann Fidanque
Illustrated by Dan McGeehan

- **This is a . . .**
- **This is not a . . .**

whale	camel	hippo

Touch under the first picture. Is it a dog? (No)
Say "this is not a dog." (This is not a dog.)
Is it a cat? (No) Say "this is not a cat." (This is not a cat.)
Is this a whale? (Yes) Say "this is a whale." (This is a whale.)

Touch under the second picture. Is it a dog? (No)
Say "this is not a dog." (This is not a dog.)
Is this a camel? (Yes) Say "this is a camel." (This is a camel.)

Touch under the next picture. Is it a cat? (No)
Say "this is not a cat." (This is not a cat.)
Is this a hippo? (Yes) Say "this is a hippo." (This is a hippo.)

UNIT 11 STORIES

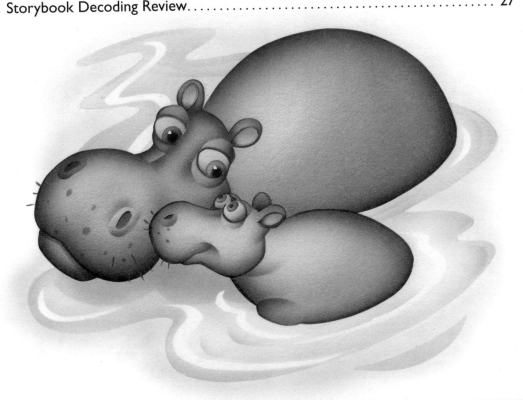

What Makes an Animal a Mammal?

CHAPTER I
Mammal Facts

What do you think this story will be about? (Mammals)
Listen carefully for four facts about mammals.

Some animals are called mammals. Mammals have a backbone and breathe air. They have hair or fur, and they take care of their babies after they are born.

Tell four facts you just learned about mammals. (They have a backbone. They breathe air. They have hair or fur, and they take care of their babies after they are born.)

Cows, tigers, squirrels, and monkeys are all mammals.

This is an .

The is an animal with a backbone.

He has a nose and breathes air.

He has a few hairs on his head.

Elephants live together and take care of their babies.

Does an elephant have a backbone? (Yes)

Does an elephant breathe air? (Yes)

Does an elephant have hair or fur? (Yes)

Look at the picture. Do you think an elephant takes care of its babies? (Yes)

So, an elephant is a . . . (mammal).

What is a mammal? Touch the animals you think are mammals and say, **"this is** a mammal," or "this is not a mammal."

Make a good guess. You may be surprised!

The , the ____, the ____, and the man are mammals.

So, what do you know about these animals? (They have backbones. They breathe air. They have hair or fur. They take care of their young.)

I knew that a whale breathed air, but I didn't know it had hair or fur. What would you like to learn about a whale? (I'd like to learn where a whale has hair.)

Look at the bird. It has no fur or hair. Instead, a bird has feathers.
A bird is not a . . . mammal. A bird is a bird.

Look at the fish. Fish do not breathe air, and they do not have fur or hair.
A fish is not a . . . mammal. A fish is a fish.

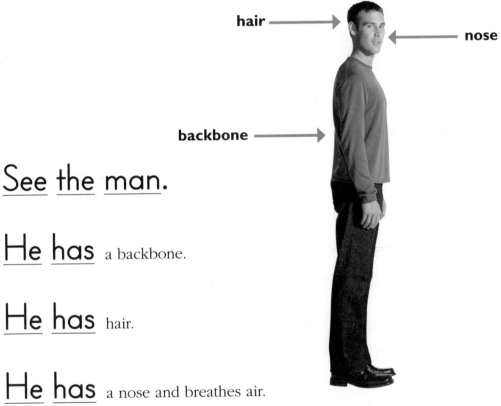

hair ———→

nose

backbone ———→

See the man.

He has a backbone.

He has hair.

He has a nose and breathes air.

When the man was young, his parents took care of him.
Now the man helps take care of his children.
So, what do you know about the man? (The man is a mammal.)
That's right. People are mammals.

Mammals can be found all over the world. Mammals live in forests, deserts, and a few mammals even live in the sea.

CHAPTER 2

The

Whales are mammals that live in the sea. These huge animals have a backbone.
They breathe air and take care of their babies.
Some people love to go whale watching.

"Meet the ," said the man.

"See him swim and swim."

"We see him!" said Nan and Dan.

"I see his ⬛," said Nan.

"I see his 2 ⬛s," said Dan.

Dan and Nan seem .

What is the whale doing? (Swimming)
Where is he swimming? (In the sea, in the ocean)
Where does the whale live? (The sea, the ocean)
If you went on a boat trip in the sea, what would you want to see?

More About Mammals

CHAPTER 1
Mammals in Their Habitats

Mammals live in special places called habitats.
What do we call the special places where mammals live? (Habitats)

The giant hippopotamus lives along the rivers of Africa.
Where does the hippo live? (Along the rivers of Africa)

<u>This is his</u> habitat.

<u>He needs</u> to stay wet and cool, so he spends his days in the river.

<u>He has his</u> eyes on top of his head so he can see.

<u>He has his</u> ears on top of his head so he can hear.

<u>He has his</u> nostrils on top of his head so he can breathe.

The hippo is well suited to live along the river where he can spend his days in the water.

Look at the picture. Touch the hippo's eyes. Where are they? (On top of his head)

Touch the hippo's ears. Where are they? (On top of his head)

Touch the hippo's nostrils. Where are they? (On top of his head)

Why do you think a hippo has his eyes, ears, and nostrils on top of his head? (So the hippo can see, hear, and breathe—even while he is in the water)

Some mammals live in a dry desert habitat. Camels live in the deserts of Africa and Asia. What is the habitat for camels? (The dry desert)

See the man with his .

The man needs the camel to work.

The camel is well suited to his desert life.

He has long eyelashes to keep the sand out of his eyes.

What keeps the sand out of the camel's eyes? (His eyelashes)
We have eyelashes too but they aren't as long. Bat your eyelashes.

He has nostrils he can close to keep the sand out.

Let's pinch our noses. That closes our nostrils.
A camel can close his nostrils to keep out the sand.

He has toes that spread out so he can walk across the sand.

He has a hump on his back. The hump stores food, not water.

Camels can live in the dry desert because they get water from the food they store.
Camels can go for months without food or water. The camel is well suited for his hot, sandy desert habitat.

What is the camel's habitat? (The hot, sandy desert)

Touch the camel's eyelashes. What do the long eyelashes do? (Keep the sand out)

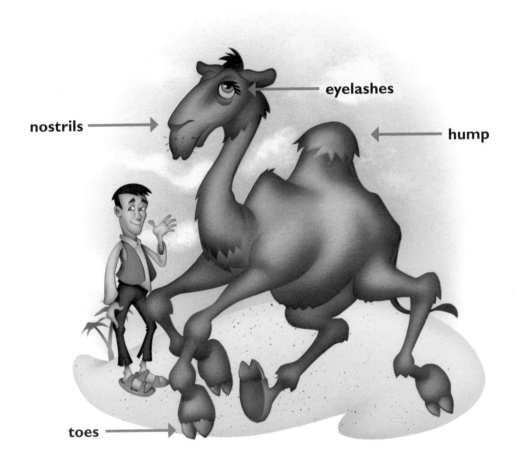

Touch the camel's nostrils. What do they do with their nostrils to keep the sand out of their noses? (They close them.)
Why do the camel's toes spread out when they walk? (It helps the camel walk on the sand.)
Touch the camel's hump. What does the camel store in its hump? (Food)
That's right. Most people think the camel stores water there, but he really stores food.

Camels can be very stubborn and ill-tempered. Some camels even spit at people!
People put up with camels because there aren't any other animals that can carry heavy loads in the desert as well as camels do.

CHAPTER 2

The  Sat

What is this chapter about? (The camel)
What do you already know about camels?

That sat in the sand.

The man said, "I need the .

He seems mad."

The said, "See me sit in the sand."

He said, "See me sit with the sad man."

What do you think the man wants the camel to help him do? (Carry a heavy load)
Why is the man sad? (The camel doesn't want to go.)

CHAPTER 3

A Hippo Named Sam

What do you think this story will be about? (A hippo named Sam)
Hippos are mammals. Listen carefully for facts that tell Sam is a mammal.

Hippos are huge and interesting mammals. They live in the rivers of Africa. We call this their habitat—the special place they live on earth.
What is a habitat? (The special place an animal lives. A hippo lives in the rivers of Africa.)

This is Sam and his mother.

Sam was just born, but he can already swim.

He swims with his mother.

He swims in the river.

Sam has fun in his river habitat.

Who is Sam? (Sam is a baby hippo.)
What can a baby hippo do? (Swim)
Who is Sam swimming with? (His mother)
Do you think Sam is a mammal? (Yes)
What fact makes you think he is a mammal? (His mother is taking care of him.)

Sam has two nostrils on the top of his head so he can breathe air while the rest of his body is under the water.

Sam has eyes on top of his head so he can see,

and he has ears on top of his head so he can hear.

Touch Sam's nostrils. Can he breathe air while he's in the water? (Yes)
How? (He breathes through the nostrils on top of his head.)
Touch Sam's eyes. Can he see while he's in the water? (Yes)
Touch Sam's ears. Can he hear while he's in the water? (Yes)
I think Sam is well suited for his river habitat.

<u>See</u> <u>Sam</u> <u>and</u> <u>his</u> herd.

The herd stays in the water during the hot day.

At night, the herd walks on the riverbank looking for food.

Sam's dad is the leader of the herd.

See Sam with his dad.

His dad is huge. He weighs as much as two cars.

How big is Sam's dad? (He is huge. He weighs as much as two cars.)
Do you think Sam will weigh that much someday?

When Sam is grown, he will eat 130 pounds of grass, leaves, and fruit each day.

What do hippos eat? (Grass, leaves, and fruit) How much do they eat? (A lot)

Perhaps one day, Sam will be the leader of his herd.

CHAPTER 4
With His Dad

What is the title of this chapter? ("With His Dad")

This is Sam.

He swims and swims.

Sam sees his dad.

He needs his dad.

Who is the story about? (Sam)
What is Sam? (A baby hippo)
Who does Sam need? (His dad)
Sam is a mammal. Baby mammals spend a lot of time with their parents.

This is Sam's dad.

Sam swims with his dad.

He and his dad swim and swim.

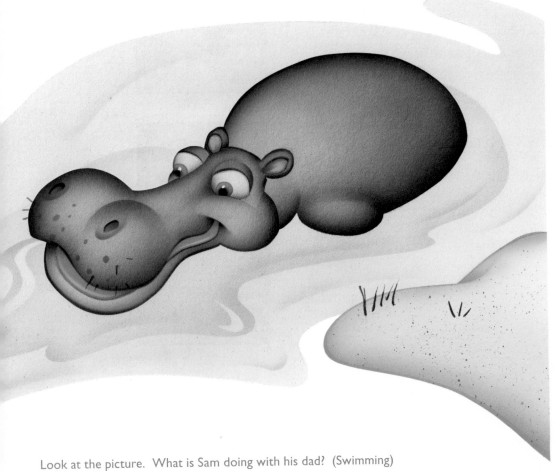

Look at the picture. What is Sam doing with his dad? (Swimming)
Why would Sam swim with his dad? (He is a mammal. Mammals stay with their parents . . .)

Facts About Mammals

Let's review some of the facts we learned about mammals.

Fact one:
Mammals have a . . . backbone.
Touch the backbone of the cat.

Fact two:
Mammals breathe . . . air.

Fact three:
Mammals have . . . fur or hair.

Fact four:
Mammals take care of their . . . babies.

Let's make a list of animals we think are mammals.
Now we can ask ourselves questions to see if they are really mammals.

Do [dogs] have a backbone?
Do [dogs] breathe air?
Do [dogs] have hair or fur?
Do [dogs] take care of their babies after they are born?

Storybook Decoding Review

Sounds you know:

■   h   a   w   i   Th

■■   ee   N   d   H   s

Words you can sound out:

●   hand   meet   swim   Dan

●●   this   He   man's   it

Words you have learned:

✈   is   has   with   Was

Sentences you can read:

✎   We had mints in the sand.

✎✎   Tim said, "His dad seems sad."

Mammal Pets

By Marilyn Sprick
Illustrated by Page O'Rourke

UNIT 12 STORIES

Vocabulary Words

cat

A cat is a small, furry animal that purrs. Cats make good pets.

dog

A dog is an animal that barks. Dogs make good pets.

skeleton

A skeleton is the part of the body that is made up of bones.

Cats and Dogs

CHAPTER I

Facts About Cats and Dogs

Many people have cats and dogs.
Raise your hand if you have a cat or dog.

This is a cat's .

The cat has a backbone.

Touch the cat's skeleton. Now touch the cat's backbone.

That is a 's .

The has a backbone too.

Touch the dog's skeleton. Now touch the dog's backbone.

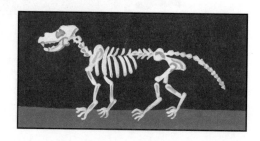

A cat breathes air.

This is a cat.

See his .

That cat has a

very sensitive nose.

Cats have a better sense
of smell than people have.
A cat can tell who someone
is by smelling them.

What can a cat tell from smelling? (Who someone is)
Is a cat's sense of smell better than yours? (Yes)

A dog breathes air.

That has a

very sensitive nose.

He can tell if an animal

is happy or mad by the animal's smell.

What can a dog tell from smelling an animal? (It can tell if the animal is happy or mad.)
Is a dog's sense of smell better than yours? (Yes)

<u>See that</u> kitten with its mother.

Just like people, mother cats will take care of their kittens. Kittens need their mothers to take care of them for at least eight weeks.

What do kittens need? (Their mothers)

<u>See that</u> puppy with its mother.

Just like cats and people, mother dogs will take care of their puppies for a long time.

What do puppies need? (Their mothers)

Facts About Cats and Dogs

We learned many facts about cats and dogs. Look at the pictures below.
What fact do these pictures show? (Cats and dogs have backbones.)

Cats and dogs breathe air.
What else do cats and dogs use their noses for? (Cats and dogs use their noses to smell food and other animals.)

Baby cats and dogs are taken care of by their parents.
What do dog and cat parents do with their babies? (They take care of them.)

Do dogs and cats have backbones?
Do dogs and cats breathe air?
Do dogs and cats take care of their babies?
Do dogs and cats have fur?

Our dog and cat friends are . . . mammals.
Many people have a dog or cat for a pet.
In the next chapter, you will read about Sam and Cass and their pets.

CHAPTER 2

<u>See</u> <u>the</u> <u>Cat</u> <u>and</u> <u>the</u>

<u>We</u> <u>see</u> <u>a</u> <u>cat</u> and a .

<u>We</u> <u>see</u> <u>Cass</u> with <u>the</u> .

<u>See</u> <u>Sam</u> <u>and</u> <u>his</u> <u>cat.</u>

Who has a dog? (Cass)
Who has a cat? (Sam)

The cat needs Sam.

Sam and his cat seem .

Why do you think the cat needs Sam?

That needs Cass.

Cass and the seem .

Why do you think the dog needs Cass?

Miss Tam's Cat

CHAPTER 1
Miss Tam

Who do you think is going to be the main character? (Miss Tam)

Meet Miss Tam.

Miss Tam was an old woman who lived in a big old house at the edge of town.

Miss Tam had a quaint and quiet life.

She planted seeds in her garden and watched the flowers grow.

Where did Miss Tam live? (In a big old house at the edge of town)
What did Miss Tam do? (Planted seeds and watched the flowers grow)

Miss Tam lived alone and liked it that way.

One day at half past two, a scruffy old tomcat appeared on Miss Tam's porch.

<u>Miss</u> <u>Tam</u> <u>sat</u> <u>in</u> her big old rocking chair reading a book.

"<u>Hiss</u>," <u>said</u> <u>the</u> <u>cat</u>.

<u>Miss</u> <u>Tam</u> <u>was</u> so surprised that she jumped ten feet up.

What did the cat do? (The cat hissed and surprised Miss Tam.)
What did Miss Tam do? (She jumped ten feet up.)

When she landed,

<u>Miss</u> <u>Tam</u> <u>said</u>, "<u>Scat</u>, <u>cat</u>!"

What do you think will happen next?

The thin and lonely cat looked sad.

Miss Tam said, "Poor old cat."

Why did Miss Tam say "Poor old cat"? (The cat looked sad, thin, and lonely.)

Miss Tam put her hand out for the cat to smell. He smelled her hand and rubbed against Miss Tam's leg. The old woman thought for a moment and said, "Okay, old fellow. Rest for a while." The cat purred; then he jumped right up into Miss Tam's lap! Before she knew it, Miss Tam found herself petting the ragged old tomcat.

The next day at half past five,

<u>Miss</u> <u>Tam</u> <u>sat</u> <u>in</u> her big old rocking chair reading a book

when the cat appeared again.

"<u>Hiss</u>," <u>said</u> <u>the</u> <u>cat</u>.

<u>Miss</u> <u>Tam</u> <u>was</u> so surprised that she jumped five feet up.

When she landed,

<u>Miss</u> <u>Tam</u> <u>said</u>, "<u>I</u> <u>said</u> <u>scat</u>!"

But then the cat smelled Miss Tam. She smelled familiar, so the cat began to purr. The old woman thought for a moment and said, "Okay, old fellow. Rest for a while."

At first, Miss Tam told the cat to . . . (scat).

Did the cat scat or go away? (No)

The cat purred and jumped right up into Miss Tam's lap. Before she knew it, Miss Tam found herself having dinner with the cat.

What did the cat do? (The cat purred; the cat ate dinner with Miss Tam.)

CHAPTER 2
See Miss Tam

What is the title of this chapter? ("See Miss Tam")

Miss Tam was with the cat.

The cat wasn't mad.

That cat was sweet.

Miss Tam said, "I see that cat.

That cat can sit with me."

Miss Tam and the cat seem .

Why do you think they seem happy?

CHAPTER 3
Miss Tam and the Cat

Who do you think this chapter will be about? (Miss Tam)
Who else is in the story? (The cat)

Miss Tam was an old woman who lived in a big old house at the edge of town. At half past two, an old cat had appeared on her porch. Miss Tam took pity on the poor cat and let him rest in her lap. At half past five, the cat came back. Miss Tam took pity on the cat and shared her dinner with him.

See Miss Tam and the cat.

Miss Tam sat in her big armchair by the fire reading a book.

At half past nine,

Miss Tam said, "That cat hasn't

budged and it is time for bed." In a small little voice,

Miss Tam said, "Scat, cat!"

Use a small little voice and say, "Scat, cat." Do you think Miss Tam really wanted the cat to leave? (No) I don't think so either. If she wanted the cat to go, she would have said it in a loud voice.

The old cat opened one eye, but he didn't budge.

Miss Tam said, "That cat isn't moving."

Then Miss Tam shrugged her shoulders and toddled up to bed.

What do you think is going to happen with the cat and Miss Tam?

The next morning at half past seven, Miss Tam fixed herself breakfast. Then she placed a bowl of eggs by her feet. With a thump, the old cat jumped down from the mantle and began eating a fine meal. Soon the cat was rubbing against Miss Tam's leg—as if to thank her.

Was the cat happy? (Yes) Why?

At noon, Miss Tam sat down to eat a tuna sandwich, and placed some tuna in a bowl by her feet. The cat purred loudly. Was the cat happy? (Yes) Why?

At dinner time, Miss Tam shared a meatloaf with the cat.

Was the cat happy? (Yes) Why?

<u>That</u> <u>cat</u> <u>was</u> soon a fat old cat.

<u>He</u> <u>wasn't</u> <u>sad</u>.

<u>He</u> <u>was</u> .

<u>Miss</u> <u>Tam</u> <u>was</u> too.

How do you think the cat felt? (Happy) Why?

How did Miss Tam feel? (Happy) Why?

I liked this story because Miss Tam and the cat found that they could make each other happy.

What did you think about the story?

45

CHAPTER 4

Meet the  Cat

What is the title of this chapter? ("Meet the Happy Cat")

"Tee hee," said Miss Tam.

"See the cat. That cat isn't sad.

That cat isn't mad. That cat is .

"See the cat and me.

He can sit with me.

We can sit and sit."

Look at the picture.

Who is the story about? (Miss Tam and the cat)

Is the cat sad? (No)

Is the cat mad? (No)

The cat is . . . (happy).

Why do you think the cat is happy?

Miss Tam's Cat

We're going to retell "Miss Tam's Cat."
What was the title of the story? ("Miss Tam's Cat")
Look at the picture. Who was the story about?
(Miss Tam and a cat)

● At the beginning of the story, what did Miss Tam
do when the scruffy old tomcat appeared on
Miss Tam's porch and hissed? (Miss Tam was
so surprised that she jumped up, then she
told the cat to scat.)

■ In the middle of the story, Miss Tam was ready
to go to bed so, in a small little voice, she told
the tomcat to scat. What happened when
Miss Tam told the cat to scat? (The cat didn't
budge so Miss Tam went to bed.)

▲ At the end of the story, what happened to the
tomcat when Miss Tam took care of him and
fed him? (The cat was soon very fat and happy,
and Miss Tam was happy too.)

Let's go back to the beginning and retell the whole story by looking at the pictures. Look at the
first picture. This story was about . . .

Storybook Decoding Review

Sounds you know:

■   C   th   a   h   ee

■■   w   D   i   c   m

Words you can sound out:

●   can   mist   We   than

●●   seed   had   tin   can't

Words you have learned:

✈   The   isn't   a   has

Sentences you can read:

✏   Nat said, "This cat is mad at me."

✏✏   He can't see his dad's hat.

Mammals in Winter

By Ann Fidanque and Marilyn Sprick
Illustrated by Jill Newton

UNIT 13 STORIES

Where to Live?

Half In and Half Out

Vocabulary Words

rabbit

A rabbit is a mammal that hops and eats carrots.

bear

A bear is a mammal with thick fur and sharp claws.

rat

A rat is a mammal that looks like a big mouse.

Where to Live?

CHAPTER 1
Winter Homes

Tad was a sweet wild rabbit.

What kind of animal was Tad? (A rabbit)

He was born in the spring.

What season was Tad born in? (In the spring)

He had lived and played in the fields all summer and fall.

Now winter was coming.

The <u>wind</u> <u>was</u> getting cold.

The <u>rats</u> <u>and</u> <u>the</u> squirrels had built nests.

Three <u>deer</u> <u>had</u> moved down the mountain.

<u>Tad</u> <u>said</u>, "<u>I</u> <u>need</u> <u>a</u> winter home too."

It was getting cold. What season was coming? (Winter)
What did the rats and squirrels do to get ready for winter? (They built nests.)
What is Tad's problem? (He needs a winter home.)

Tad saw a snake slither under a rock. "That looks like a nice winter home," said Tad. So Tad tried to join the snake underneath the rock.
What do you think the snake thought about Tad joining him under the rock?

"Hiss," said the snake. "Go away!"
What did the snake say to Tad? (Go away)

Tad ran as fast as he could.

Then Tad saw a toad who had buried herself in the mud to stay warm.

"Can I sit with you in the mud through the long winter

months?" asked Tad.

What was the toad doing to stay warm in the winter? (She was sitting in the mud.)
Do you think Tad should sit in the mud all winter long?

"What?" asked the toad.

"**I** **want** to sit in the mud," said Tad.

"**I** **want** **a** nice warm place to stay for the cold winter months."

What did Tad want to do? (Sit in the mud; find a warm place for winter)

The toad said, "Silly rabbit. You do not want to sit in the mud with me. You have a beautiful fur coat that will keep you warm through the cold winter months. You can still run and play. Rabbits in fur coats don't need a special winter home."

In the end, what did Tad learn? (He learned that rabbits don't need special winter homes because they have thick fur.)

CHAPTER 2
The Wind

What is the title of this chapter? ("The Wind")

The wind said, "Www, w, w."

What did the wind say? (The wind said, "Www, w, w.")

The deer ran.

What did the deer do? (The deer ran.)

He said, "I need the ."

The wind said, "Www, w, w."

Three rats hid in a tree.

What did the three rats do? (The three rats hid in a tree.)

The wind said, "Www, w, w."

The cat sat in the .

What did the cat do? (The cat sat in the house.)

Half In and Half Out

CHAPTER I
Getting Ready for Winter

What do you think is going to happen in this story?

Before the long winter comes, bears store fat so they can sleep through the cold winter months. With winter on its way, Tim the bear was hungry—as hungry as a bear!

"Rrr, rrr, rrr," growled Tim.

"I want that meat."

Tim ran and ran for his lunch but the mouse ran faster.

Who is the story about? (Tim the bear)
What did Tim say he wanted to eat? (Meat, the mouse)

"<u>Rrr</u>, <u>rrr</u>, <u>rrr</u>," growled Tim.

"<u>I</u> <u>can</u> <u>eat</u> <u>a</u> ."

What did Tim say he could eat? (A fish)

<u>Tim</u> <u>swam</u> <u>and</u> <u>swam</u> for his lunch.

He caught a large fish, but Tim was still very hungry—as hungry as a bear!

How hungry was Tim after he ate the fish? (Very hungry, as hungry as a bear)

59

Then Tim saw a beehive in a tree on a far-off hill.
What did Tim see in the tree on the hill? (A beehive)

Tim ran and ran.

"Rrr, rrr, rrr," growled Tim.

"I see sweets in that tree," said Tim.

"I can eat sweets!"

Tim climbed the tree and helped himself to the honey. Tim grew fatter and fatter, but Tim was still hungry—as hungry as a bear!
How hungry was Tim after he ate the honey? (As hungry as a bear)

CHAPTER 2
Hungry as a Bear

The man said, "I can see a ."

The man ran and hid.

What did the man see? (A bear)
What did the man do? (He ran and hid.)

Tim said, "I want meat!

I see three hams.

The ham is near that tree.

I can eat, eat, eat.

Mmm, mmm, mmm."

What did Tim want? (Meat)
What did Tim see? (Three hams)
What do you think Tim will do with the hams? (He will eat them.)

CHAPTER 3
Stuck

At last, winter came. Snow fell gently on the forest, and Tim was finally satisfied. He had stored huge rolls of fat.

How hungry was Tim when winter finally came? (He wasn't hungry anymore.)

Tim said, "I had meat.

I had sweets. This is the time for me to sleep!"

What did Tim want to do in the winter? (He wanted to sleep.)

Then Tim slowly waddled off to his winter cave. When Tim tried to crawl in his cave, he was in for a surprise!

What do you think the surprise was?

Tim said, "I can't get in.

I can't get out."

Poor Tim! He was half in and half out!

He was stuck!

What is Tim's problem? (He was stuck half in and half out of his cave.)

"Tee hee!" said a rat.

"This bear is stuck—half in and half out. I think this cave will make a fine winter home for me."

What did the rat think? (He thought the cave would make a fine home for him.)

Tim didn't say a thing. He just yawned and fell asleep.

What did Tim do? (Tim just yawned and fell asleep.)

The rat ran about busily setting up house.

Soon the rat was ready to take a nap.
Just as the rat laid down to rest, Tim began to snore.

"<u>S</u>ss, <u>sss</u>, <u>sss</u>," snored Tim.

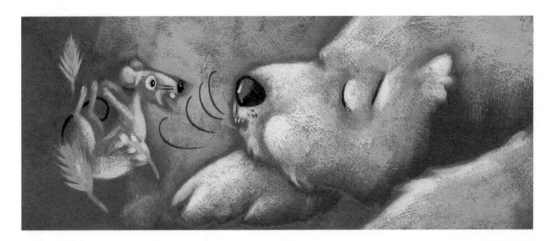

"<u>Rats!</u>" said <u>the</u> <u>mad</u> <u>rat</u> <u>as</u> <u>he</u> <u>was</u>

thrown into the air. "I can't stay here. I won't survive."
What happened when the rat laid down to rest?
(The rat was thrown into the air by Tim's snoring. He decided to leave.)

The rat moved out and Tim slept peacefully—half in his cave and half out,
getting thinner and thinner all winter long, until spring came.
What happened in the end?
(The rat moved out of the cave, and Tim slept peacefully.)

CHAPTER 4
Tim

What is the title of this chapter? ("Tim")

Tim said, "I see the .

I can eat. I want meat."

Who is the story about? (Tim, the bear)
What did Tim want to do when the sun was warm again? (He wanted to eat meat.)

The rat said, "Tim wants meat.

Rats! I am meat."

See that rat. He ran and ran.

The rat ran and hid!

Why did the rat run and hide? (He didn't want Tim to eat him.)

Tim didn't see the rat.

Did Tim see the rat in the end? (No)

Half In and Half Out

We're going to retell "Half In and Half Out."

What was the title of the story? ("Half In and Half Out")

Look at the picture below. Who was the story about? (Tim)

● At the beginning of the story, what did Tim the bear do to get ready to sleep through the cold winter? (Tim ate and ate; Tim ate fish, ham, and honey.)

■ In the middle of the story, Tim had stored huge rolls of fat. He was ready to sleep for the winter. What happened to Tim when he tried to crawl in his cave? (He was so fat he got stuck.)

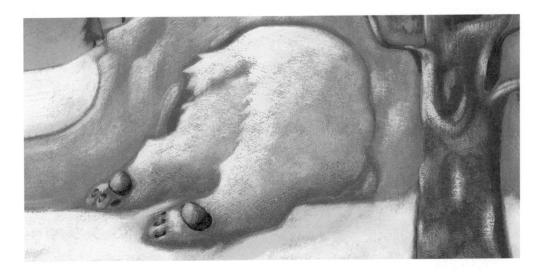

▲ What happened at the end of the story? (Tim woke up when the sun was warm again and he wanted to eat—he wanted meat.)

Let's go back to the beginning and retell the whole story by looking at the pictures. Look at the first picture. This story was about . . .

Storybook Decoding Review

Sounds you know:

■   R   W   i   C   A

■■   t   ea   r   H   e

Words you can sound out:

●   meat   rats   three   hand

●●   this   deer   cat   tree

Words you have learned:

✈   wasn't   The   want   his

Sentences you can read:

✎   I said, "We ran in the mist."

✎✎   Can we eat with him?